Boxes, Baskets and Platforms

Artificial nest sites for owls and other birds of prey

Sue M. Dewar

Colin R. Shawyer

London

The Hawk and Owl Trust, c/o Zoological Society of London, Regent's Park, London NW1 4RY

e-mail: hawkandowltrust@aol.com

website: hawkandowl.org

A catalogue record for this book is available from the British Library

ISBN 0–9503187–6–0

Design and Production:

Printed by: Arlequin Press, 26 Broomfield Road, Chelmsford, Essex CM1 1SW
Telephone: 01245 267771

Acknowledgements:
Philip Burton, Nick Dixon, David and Don Garner, Barbara Hall, Barry Ingram, Paul Johnson, Roy Leigh, Graham Lenton, Archie Simpson, Alan Skates, the late Robin Spencer and Chris Sperring.

Introduction

In 1988 The Hawk and Owl Trust, as part of its conservation strategy for the Barn Owl, set up its national habitat restoration plan — ***The Farmland, Riverside and Forestry Link Initiative***. Having identified areas in Britain where Barn Owls still remained, the Trust's first task was to consolidate remnant and hence fragile populations and then re-establish these birds throughout Britain by developing a national network of habitat corridors to link isolated strongholds. This initiative was designed so as to create prey-rich hunting grounds and artificial nesting sites in a manner which could provide habitat continuity, farm to farm and county to county.

This initiative, which in the 1980s was the first of its kind, is now enjoying considerable success throughout Britain. In some places Barn Owl numbers have at least doubled and in others they have trebled. Viable breeding populations have become established on newly created habitat corridors in places where previously these owls were unknown.

Meeting the Challenge

Given enough help and sufficient funds, the Trust has little doubt that it has the necessary knowledge and expertise to enable it to increase the Barn Owl population in the British Isles by at least one half during the next 20 years. This is the target of the RSPB/JNCC Species Action Plan contained in *Biodiversity Challenge*, a contribution by voluntary conservation bodies to the Government's *Biodiversity: UK Action Plan*.

Why Help is Needed

Dutch Elm disease, the felling of many hollow trees for safety reasons, and severe gales, has accounted for the loss of many natural nesting sites for birds, particularly cavity nesting species such as the Barn Owl, Little Owl *Athene noctua*, Tawny Owl *Strix aluco* and Kestrel. In addition, the conversion or demolition of old farm buildings has meant that many traditional nest sites have disappeared.

Working in Partnership

Since the Trust began its ***Link Initiative*** it has become increasingly involved in extensive habitat restoration projects, not only with individual farmers but with local authorities, water companies, private estates, golf courses, commercial forests and organisations such as the Environment Agency, drainage boards and the Crown Estate. Habitat reinstatement and the resultant increase in food supply is central to the success of any scheme which involves the use of boxes, baskets or platforms as artificial nesting sites. This is particularly true for the Barn Owl, Kestrel, Little Owl and Long-eared Owl (the first three of which are now listed as being of Conservation Concern in Europe). Indeed, these birds represent "flagships" for the conservation of habitats supporting a variety of wildlife, from plants and insects to bats and larger mammals.

Providing the Best

The nest box and platform designs described in this booklet are the result of many years' research and development by the authors and have been optimised to take into account the specific needs of each species. When carefully sited they can produce more young than natural sites which are often of lesser quality because they are less secure, exposed to rain and wind and commonly situated at some distance from the birds' favoured hunting grounds.

Originally The Hawk and Owl Trust's nest boxes were made by the late Harry Shawyer. Because the Trust now installs about 1,000 boxes every year they are manufactured commercially to the author's designs.

This booklet has been written to enable the Trust to share the knowledge it has gained in habitat restoration and the design and siting of artificial nest sites for owls and other birds of prey.

Before you begin

Achieving Success

Success depends on carefully targeting artificial nest sites for owls and other birds of prey into their appropriate habitats, rich in prey. In some places the Trust undertakes a survey of potential prey species before it begins. **If these habitats are not available, then they must be created and managed.**

As a general rule large areas of rank open grassland or farmland intersected by rivers, streams and ditches are the preferred habitats of Barn Owl and Kestrel, while mown or grazed grassland and old orchards are well suited to the Little Owl. On the other hand, woodland or dense forest is the home of the Tawny Owl and Goshawk *Accipiter gentilis*. The Hobby *Falco subbuteo* prefers small patches of tall trees or an isolated tree on open farmland or heathland, often near water. Smaller woodland copses, shelter belts and areas of mature scrub adjacent to open grassland or moorland are especially favoured by Long-eared Owl, Buzzard and Merlin. Although most Peregrines *Falco peregrinus* in Britain are cliff-nesting, they are increasingly moving into more urban areas where pigeons, their favoured prey, are often very common. The Osprey *Pandion haliaetus* will only nest near lakes, lochs and reservoirs where fish stocks are high, so nest platforms for this species are only relevant in special situations.

Materials and Design

One of the main considerations when choosing materials for nest boxes is for long-term durability. However, boxes made from heavy timber can be difficult and dangerous to install because of their weight. For this reason the Trust favours boxes made from 9mm (⅜″) exterior grade plywood, braced inside with softwood battens. Apple crates and old ammunition boxes can provide inexpensive alternatives but are normally impossible for one person to install and often need to be winched into place by at least two people using rope and pulley.

Large plastic drums have been used as artificial nest sites in trees, particularly for Barn Owls, but early research by the authors indicated that they produce fewer young than well-made wooden boxes. This is because in warm conditions condensation forms on the inner walls causing them to run with water, while on dry cold nights the drums chill rapidly. Both of these conditions are less than ideal for the incubation of eggs and the development of young. However, success can be achieved when using plastic drums in buildings because the effects of the weather are of less consequence.

Boxes should have several 7mm (¼″) holes drilled in their base to provide drainage. About 50mm (2″) of untreated wood chippings or crushed tree bark must be placed inside to enable the birds to form a scrape. Peat can get very wet and can clog the drain holes, while straw should not be used since it sometimes contains fungal spores which can prove fatal to birds. Covering the box with roofing felt is not recommended as this prevents the timber from "breathing" and can shorten the life of the box.

Boxes which are not designed with open fronts should be provided with inspection doors or panels of sufficient size (at least 250mm [10″] square) to allow debris such as old Jackdaw *Corvus monedula* nests to be removed easily. The doors can be hung with brass or nylon hinges or a 50mm (2″) wide strip of rubber, secured at the bottom with a draw bolt or hook and eye. The Trust has recently developed a more simple but effective hinge. This involves hanging the door at the top by drilling three 4mm (⅛″) holes in the edge of the door and three alongside in the box frame. Three plastic cable-ties are then passed through the holes and pulled tight to form a hinge. The door can also be secured in the same way using one or two cable-ties at the bottom. Although these bottom ties will need to be removed with cutters and replaced every time the box is inspected, this method, as well as being cheap and maintenance free, prevents unauthorised inspection by casual observers who would not normally have cutters to hand.

Treatment of the Wood

The Trust uses plywood sheets which have been pre-treated with water-based wood preservative. After the box has been constructed it can then be surface-treated with a wax-like coating *(Sikkens or Sadolin)* which renders the box maintenance-free for a number of years.

The Trust is constantly trying to improve the durability of its wooden nest boxes and a development by one of its BOCN Advisors has been to coat the wooden carcase with fibre-glass resin. These boxes are currently being used on Vodafone transmission masts.

Choosing a Site

It is a common misconception that birds of prey need boxes which are positioned on the highest parts of a tree or building. Ideally boxes only need to be sited at a height of between 3-5m (10-16′), one which most two-stage ladders can easily reach but which discourages casual inspection by members of the public. Baskets and platforms on the other hand, need to be installed at a greater height than boxes in order to attract the birds for which they are intended *(see illustration)*.

Where to site boxes, baskets and platforms

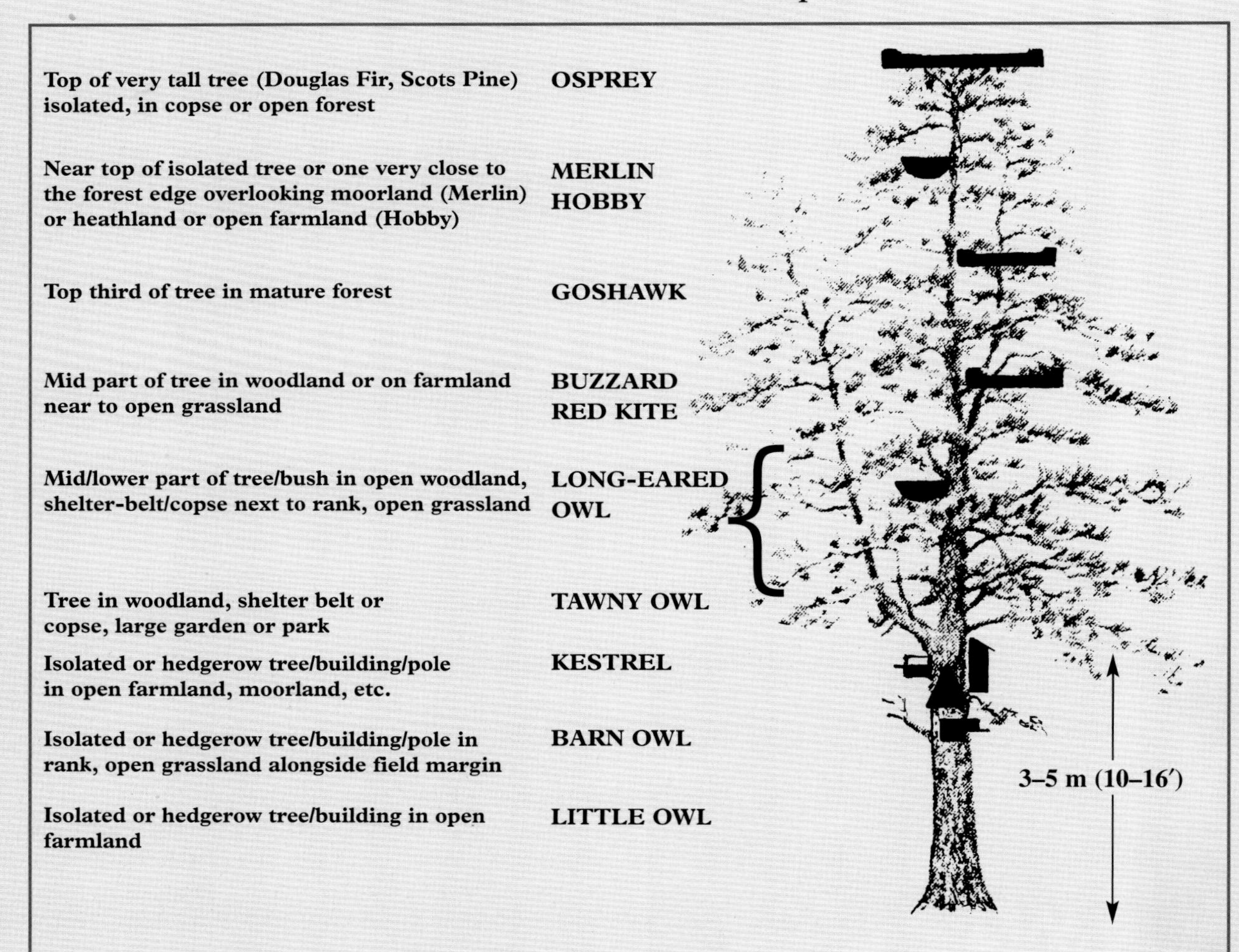

Birds of prey nest in coniferous or deciduous trees although the Osprey usually prefers a tall and exposed tree such as Douglas Fir or Scots Pine. Closely planted trees in densely-packed commercial spruce forests are usually unsuitable. Select a tree close to a woodland path or ride to provide the birds with a clear flight path.

Nest boxes for all but the Tawny Owl, which prefers to nest in woodland, should face onto open land. They should not be obscured by tree foliage or thick ivy; the more obvious they are the better. If sites are likely to become overgrown by ivy or tall scrub, this should be removed with a bow saw before the box is installed. **When installing boxes during the winter it is important to remember that they may become less obvious to the birds when the tree is fully in leaf**. Where possible the entrance hole of the box should face away from the prevailing wind and direct rain. All boxes are designed to include an opening near the top of the box to help prevent young owls falling out, (this sometimes occurs in Barn Owls during years when food is scarce). All have a large exercise platform or perch.

Artificial nest sites are best installed before the end of November to give the best chance of success the following year. It can take three years or more before a site is used for nesting, although there are often encouraging signs of roosting, such as a build-up of pellets or feathers, before then.

Installing the Box

The Trust has pioneered the use of non-metallic fixings such as plastic cable-ties and nylon bolts, and now uses them routinely when installing boxes and baskets in living trees.

These materials minimise damage to timber. Also, if felling takes place in the future, these fixings present no hazard to chainsaw operators and those carrying out mechanised harvesting. For this reason, the wooden mounting boards used to secure tree boxes are primarily designed for these more specialised forms of attachment but also include pre-drilled holes for more traditional fixing methods, using nails. This style of mounting board is used by the authors for installing nest boxes. In the Barn Owl 'A'-frame box and the Tawny Owl box the mounting board forms an integral part of their construction, while in the Kestrel and Little Owl designs it is screwed onto the side of the box at the time of installation.

To install nest boxes with nylon bolts it is best to select an upright tree trunk with a flat face, free of knobbles and projections. The tree is then pre-drilled with a high-powered (24-volt)

Mounting board (for Kestrel and Little Owl boxes)

Pre-drilled holes for nail fixing

'Keyhole' to enable box to be hung on nylon bolt.

Pilot holes for screwing board to box

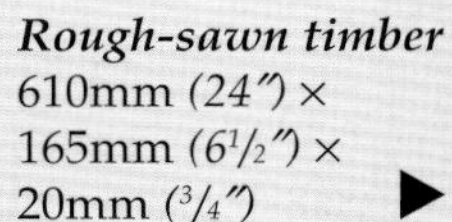

Rough-sawn timber
610mm (24″) ×
165mm (6½″) ×
20mm (¾″) ▶

rechargeable drill fitted with a 14mm wood-boring auger bit to a depth of about 38mm (1½″). A 15mm dia., 100mm long nylon hexagon-head bolt is screwed into the hole with a wrench and socket. The box is then hung onto the bolt through the pre-cut keyhole at the top of the mounting board. The head of the bolt is then cut off with a hacksaw. A further hole is then drilled into the tree through the bottom hole in the mounting board, and a second bolt inserted, tightened and the head removed. Two nylon washer-faced nuts are then tightened onto the stubs of the protruding bolts. They can be slackened off each year as the tree grows. If the boxes are fixed too rigidly they distort very quickly and eventually break apart, particularly on fast-growing trees such as poplar, willow and sycamore. These trees should be avoided when possible.

If birds have made no attempt to use a box after three or four years it may be useful to consider moving the box to another location. The nylon nut and bolt method allows this to be carried out easily. Nest baskets and platforms should be secured in trees with plastic cable-ties.

Integral mounting board in Barn Owl 'A'-frame box

Separate mounting board screwed to Kestrel box

NEST BOXES

Barn Owl

The Barn Owl remains a scarce bird in Britain and Ireland numbering about 5,000 pairs having declined by 70% between 1932 and 1985. Changes in farming methods and increased urbanisation have resulted in the loss and fragmentation of suitable foraging habitat. Small fields enclosed by hedgerows with wide grassy margins have largely been replaced by prairie-type fields surrounded by fences which offer trouble-free maintenance and easy access for the farm machinery. In addition, traditional farmyards, where rodents once flourished in the barns and stackyards which held unthreshed grain, have given way to rodent-proof silos and internal storage bins. Major increases in the stocking density of sheep and silage production, particularly in south-west Britain, render many grasslands useless for the Barn Owl because the short turf provides unsuitable habitat for the small mammals on which this owl feeds.

Many natural Barn Owl nest sites have disappeared over the years. In the last century barns were built with Barn Owl "windows" to encourage owls to nest inside on the sheaves of unthreshed corn and help control rodents. Today many of these barns are now used for storing farm machinery and provide few suitable nesting places; others have disintegrated or been converted, to be replaced by modern barns. To add to these problems a combination of storm-force gales, Dutch Elm disease and the felling of many hollow trees for safety reasons reduced the number of natural nesting cavities.

Measures such as the Trust's own ***Farmland, Riverside and Forestry Link Initiative***, and others such as non-rotational Set-aside and Countryside Stewardship are gradually increasing the foraging habitat, in the form of

"tussocky" grassland corridors and field margins which supply the right conditions for voles, shrews and mice — the staple diet of the Barn Owl. Once these habitats have been created, suitable nesting sites may be absent. It is therefore important that nest boxes are installed to provide additional roost sites to encourage the birds to breed. **However, the provision of nest boxes alone will never attract Barn Owls back into an area where there is insufficient foraging habitat**.

Barn Owls prefer to breed at altitudes less than 160m (500′) above sea level. They are not found in dense woodland, preferring open land and the woodland edge where grassland is tussocky and rank.

These owls does not hoot, but utter a long drawn-out rasping screech. Despite its name, the Barn Owl will nest in a wide variety of situations, but always prefers roomy and well-sheltered places free from excessive human disturbance. Barns both old and modern are used but only if they provide wide ledges, wall cavities, spaces among bales of hay or straw, or nest boxes. Spacious tree cavities are also a favoured nesting site, particularly in eastern England.

Like all owls, Barn Owls make no nest but lay on average five eggs, usually on a cushion of discarded pellets. Eggs are commonly laid in late April or early May, and each egg hatches after 31 days, two or three days apart. The young remain in the nest for nine weeks or longer, rarely leaving until late July or August. In years of high food abundance, breeding can begin earlier and two broods are sometimes reared but usually at different nest sites.

Boxes not only provide suitable nesting quarters, but offer additional roosting sites which are also very important if Barn Owls are to be attracted to an area. Boxes are most successful on farms where Barn Owls have been seen, or in places where they are already known to roost. Occupied roosting sites can be recognised by long streaks of "whitewash" on the beams and black pellets about the size of a human thumb which the owl ejects from its mouth, onto the floor beneath. Evidence like this readily identifies a favoured roosting place.

Which Box to Choose

Of all the various box designs, pole boxes are usually the most successful, followed by tree boxes and then interior boxes. The one exception to this is when an interior box is placed at an existing Barn Owl roost site when it can readily be taken up for nesting. Interior nest boxes can also be more successful than outdoor ones in areas where there is an abundance of Jackdaws, since these birds will readily take over boxes on poles or trees but are more reluctant to venture far within darkened farm buildings.

Interior Boxes

Because Barn Owls can produce large broods and their young occupy the nest for a long period, they require very spacious nesting quarters. Tea chests can make ideal nest boxes in sheltered farm buildings. The floor section should be reinforced with an extended board which also provides a wide ledge at the front beneath the entrance hole. This hole, about 150mm × 150mm (6″ × 6″), should be cut in the top corner of the front panel. Interior boxes can be tailor made, and should have an internal floor area of at least 600mm × 450mm (24″ × 18″) and a height of 450mm (18″). Tea chests are light and manageable but purpose-made boxes, although heavy and difficult to install, will last much longer.

The building selected must have permanent access through an open doorway, window or ventilation slit and this should be not less than 150mm (6″) square. Barn Owls prefer to have at least two means of entry and exit from the building, together with an uninterrupted flight to the box, with open-fronted buildings being favoured. Boxes can be nailed in place or secured with long cable-ties on a beam or wall support high up in the dark roof space of a farm building, away from repeated human movements. The entrance should face at right angles to any prevailing wind, strong draught or the main light source. A layer of wood chippings or crushed bark about 50mm (2″) deep should be placed inside the box to provide a cushion for the eggs. Unlike exterior boxes, indoor boxes do not require an interior baffle board when they are positioned in a sheltered and dark position within the building.

Hay Barns – old and modern

In timber, stone or brick barns, boxes are best secured high up in a secluded area, preferably on an inside gable.

In open steel, or concrete/asbestos barns where boxes cannot be nailed in place, fixing can be more difficult. It is a good idea to screw two long wooden spars (50mm × 20mm [2″×¾″]) vertically on the side of the box, carefully spaced so that they can slip down the gaps between the corrugated wall panels and a horizontal wall brace *(see picture page 18)*. The box then becomes self-supporting. If this is not possible, support for the box can be provided by two lengths of 50–100mm (2″–4″) timber supported at their ends across one corner of the barn, on the concrete or steel wall braces, strapped in place with cable-ties.

Companies specialising in prefabricated farm buildings are encouraged to include self-contained nesting boxes. *The Trust can give advice and suitable designs to manufacturers or suppliers for such a purpose.* When erecting boxes in barns which have asbestos or metal roofs, it is important to leave a space of at least 1m (3'3") between the top of the box and the roof to reduce the risk of the nest box overheating during hot summers.

Boxes are heavy, so where possible it is best to erect them in hay barns when the building is full of bales, allowing easier access to the roof space. It is advantageous to retain a stack of bales beneath and around the nest box from February to August and, if at all possible, throughout the year. This provides additional seclusion and greater safety for the young owlets to exercise as they leave the nest.

Bale Stacks

One way of providing secluded nest sites in hay barns is by substituting a bale for a purpose-made box, **but only when a wall of bales will remain intact throughout the breeding season.** This box can be incorporated at the time the bale stack is constructed during the autumn in preparation for nesting the following spring. As Kestrels also use these boxes, two should be incorporated within the bale stack, one along the south side, the other along the south-east face, ensuring that cats are unable to gain easy access.

Storage Barns

Under the Department for Environment, Food and Rural Affairs (DEFRA) guidelines for the control of salmonella in animal feeding stuffs, it is no longer advisable to encourage wildlife into barns used for storing grain and other food. In food storage barns or in the roof space of an occupied building to which Barn Owls cannot be allowed complete access, a nest box can be backed up against an entry hole in the wall. Any gaps around the box can be plugged with wire mesh to prevent owls and other smaller birds getting into the building itself. Alternatively a permanent owl loft can be constructed.

Renovated Buildings

Creating an owl window

Before chemical poisons were available, farmers relied on natural predators such as cats and Barn Owls to help control the numbers of rodents. Many old hay barns were designed and built with owl windows: small openings high in the gable end through which the owls could fly. These windows were sometimes very ornate, some incorporating a small landing ledge at their base.

With the current reliance upon chemical poisons (rodenticides) for rodent control, many owl windows have been blocked and new farm buildings are built with no provision for the birds to enter. Traditionally, Barn Owls favour roosting and nesting within buildings where they can gain shelter from the weather, and in winter can feed on mice and rats which take up residence at that time of the year. Without access however, Barn Owls are unable to take advantage of the shelter and food that farm buildings afford.

As an adult Barn Owl stands approximately 330mm (13") tall, it is important that the hole is large enough for it to enter. A landing platform assists the birds, particularly when they are alighting with prey. It also helps inexperienced young birds to return safely to the barn for food until they become fully independent.

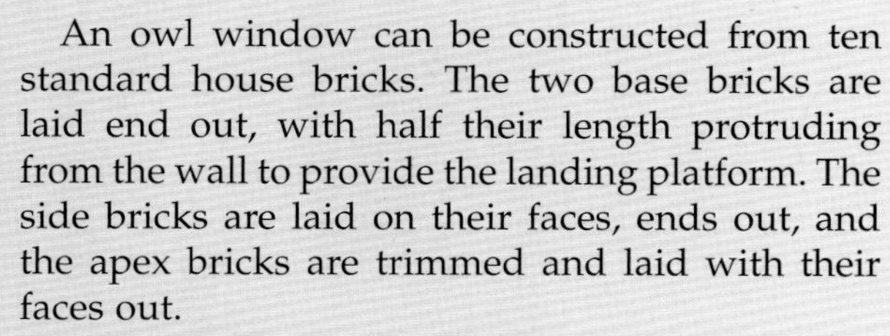

An owl window can be constructed from ten standard house bricks. The two base bricks are laid end out, with half their length protruding from the wall to provide the landing platform. The side bricks are laid on their faces, ends out, and the apex bricks are trimmed and laid with their faces out.

Owl windows should be positioned about 900mm (3′) below the apex of the gable end. This allows for an owl loft to be constructed behind the hole, or a nest box to be installed in the barn, on a beam alongside the owl window.

Constructing an owl loft

Barn Owls are often reluctant to occupy farm buildings which have been modernised or converted. Where Barn Owls are likely to be displaced because of renovation, specially designed "lofts" should be included in the apex. The entrance to these lofts should be constructed at the end of the building least disturbed by human activity *(The Hawk and Owl Trust provides a special leaflet on this subject).*

It is usually quite straightforward to board off a small area beneath the apex of the barn roof to provide a floor area which should be a minimum of 900mm (3′) long and 600mm (2′) wide. The back of the loft can then be panelled off and an inspection door provided to enable the loft to be cleaned out occasionally. The base and end panel can then be covered on their outside surfaces with insulation board.

Because Barn Owls do not construct a true nest but often use their own pellets as a lining on which to lay their eggs, a two inch layer of wood chippings or crushed bark should be placed on the floor of the nest box or loft.

Owl windows and lofts pioneered by The Hawk and Owl Trust in 1982 are now being used successfully in converted farm buildings and warehouses throughout Britain.

Exterior Boxes

On Trees

Although the Barn Owl is not a woodland bird, nest boxes are highly successful when erected in

an **isolated** hedgerow, parkland or farmland tree, or when placed on a tree around the woodland edge. The box should not be hidden by foliage and should be highly visible when the tree is in full leaf; the more obvious the better. A number of different box designs have been used by the authors over the years. We recommend an 'A'-frame box which is best positioned on an isolated tree against the main trunk, or in the crown of a pollarded tree. The boxes are fixed (with their front panels detached) through the integral mounting board using the methods described earlier in this booklet.

External Barn Owl boxes are designed to offer a dark, sheltered chamber which simulates a tree

cavity. Provision for fledglings to exercise is made by incorporating a large landing ledge.

Other designs can be used, but external boxes must be weatherproof and an apex roof with a rainshield is advisable to reduce water seepage into the box.

Boxes on Poles

In prey-rich grassland habitats which lack suitable buildings or sturdy, isolated trees, pole-mounted boxes are giving exceptional results and are greatly assisting the expansion of the Barn Owl population. This success can be attributed to the fact that they are quickly spotted by Barn Owls, can be installed within the best feeding areas. Paired boxes can be spaced every 1–2k (1½ miles), thereby maximising nesting density. Critically important in these exposed, outdoor boxes is an internal baffle which divides the interior of the box to provide a draught-free nesting chamber on one side and an exercising compartment on the other.

The boxes illustrated below and opposite are designed with an upper and lower chamber, each with its own entry hole. This provides a separate roost site for the male Barn Owl in the top chamber (since he is not normally tolerated by the nesting female once the young hatch) but allows him to be close enough to defend his mate. The Trust erects these boxes in pairs on separate poles about 18–45m (20–50 yards) apart. This provides sites for both Kestrels and Barn Owls and in most schemes the paired boxes are commonly used in this way.

Pole boxes are large and very heavy. Hoisting the pole safely with the box attached requires great care and careful planning to achieve a firm footing. The Trust employs a specialist contractor to undertake the work, which involves sinking the 150mm (6″) diameter "telegraph" poles 1½m (5′) in the ground. Ladder guides are attached to the outside of the box next to the inspection door using coach bolts, so that future monitoring and maintenance can be carried out safely.

Any organisation contemplating a network of pole boxes of this type is advised to engage the Trust to manufacture the brackets and boxes and undertake the installation since it is a highly specialised operation (see page 14).

A simplified design is illustrated below and plans are provided on page 24 for those who wish to install their own pole box. The box can be made from a single sheet of plywood and can be attached to a less substantial pole than the ones used into Trusts' own schemes.

Because this box and pole is much lighter it can be hoisted into place by hand and installed in a hole which has been hand dug to a depth of about 1m (3′3″).

This simplified pole box design is not recommended for schemes involving more than two boxes, since it does not meet the necessary specifications for longevity or safety which is needed for large schemes of the type the Trust conducts, for example with the Environment Agency, Crown Estate, Internal Drainage Boards, etc.

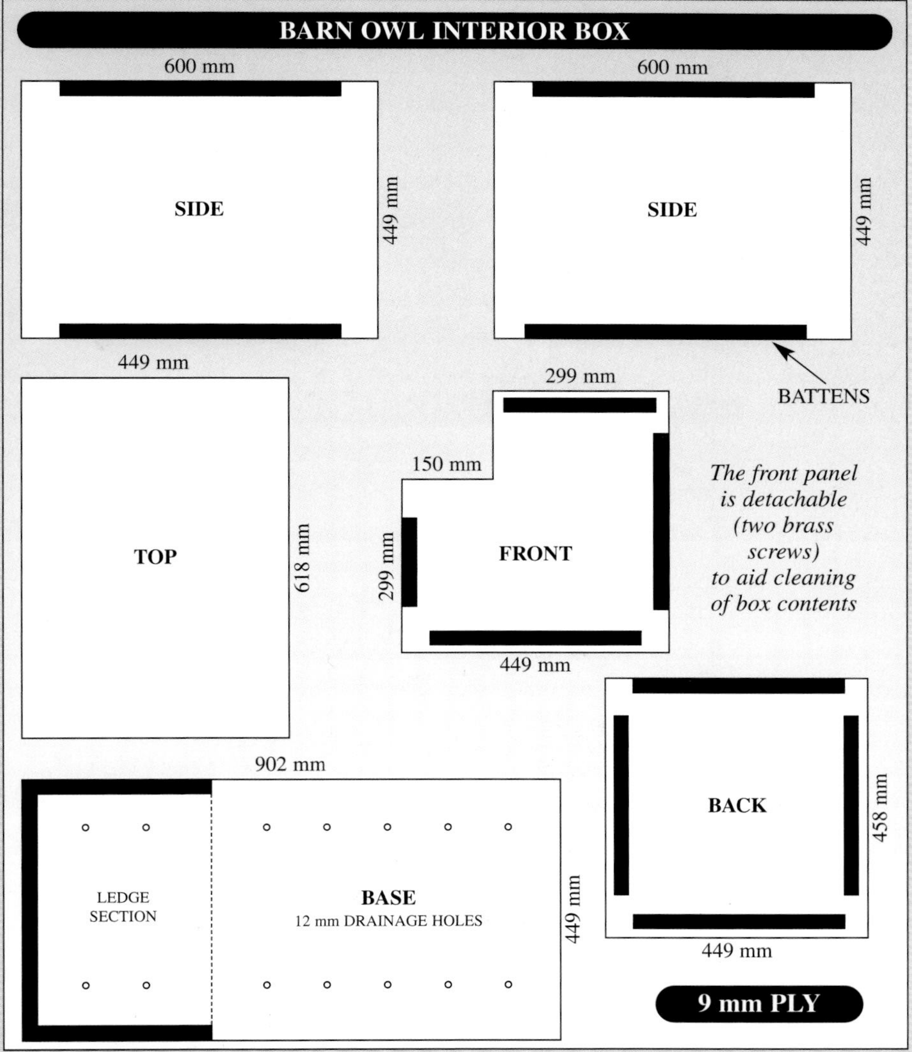
BARN OWL INTERIOR BOX
600 mm
SIDE
449 mm
600 mm
SIDE
449 mm
BATTENS
449 mm
TOP
618 mm
299 mm
150 mm
299 mm
FRONT
449 mm
The front panel is detachable (two brass screws) to aid cleaning of box contents
902 mm
LEDGE SECTION
BASE
12 mm DRAINAGE HOLES
449 mm
BACK
458 mm
449 mm
9 mm PLY

INSTALLATION

The front is screwed on after the box has been attached to the tree using two 15mm nylon bolts which pass through the integral mounting board.

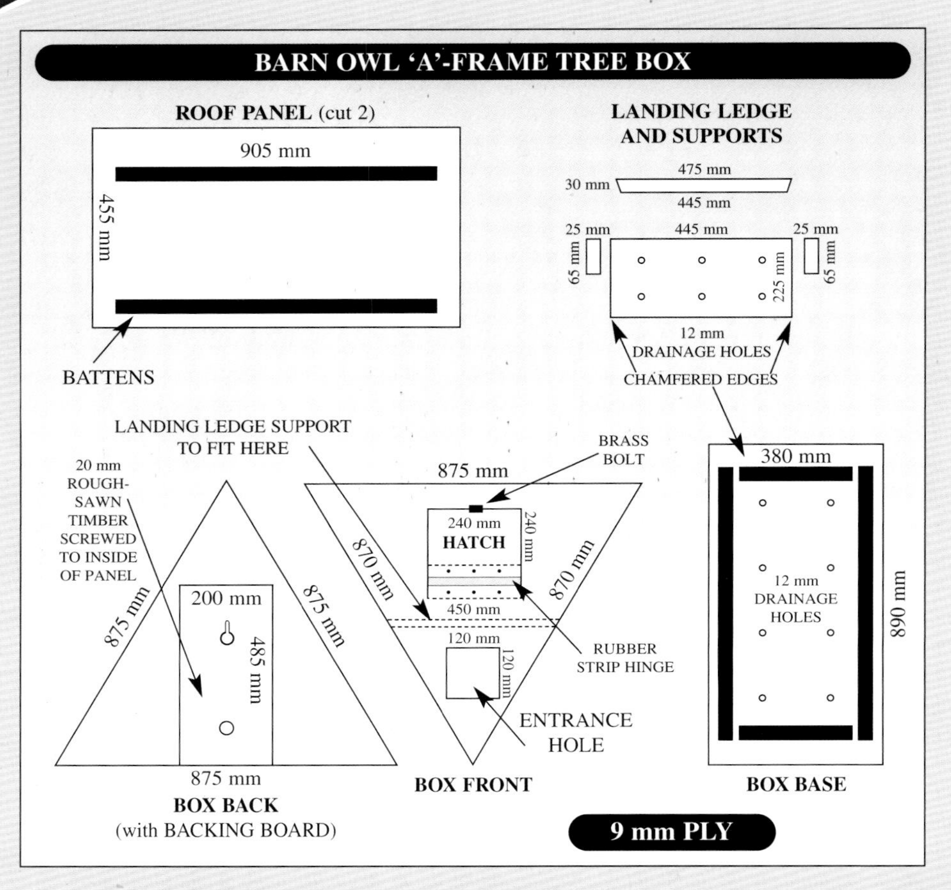

CUTTING PLAN

requires one 2440mm x 1220 mm (8′×4′) sheet of 12mm (½″) exterior ply. The rear panel has a 255mm × 255mm (10″×10″) inspection hatch in rear panel with a door. The interior baffle runs front to rear screening the larger nest chamber; the space above it aids ventilation.

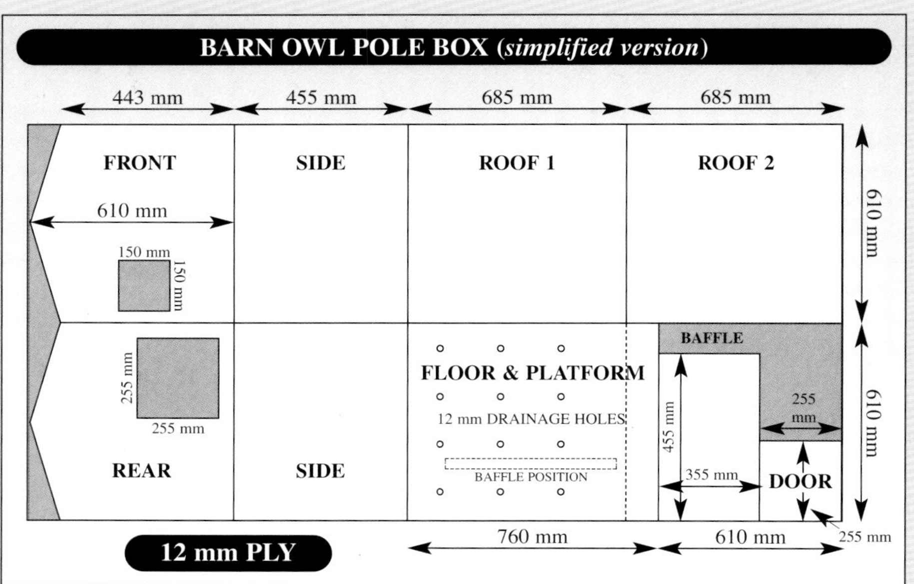

Tawny Owl

Although the Tawny Owl is not known to have bred in Ireland, the Isle of Man or on the Isle of Wight because it is rarely capable of crossing water, it is the most common owl in England, Scotland and Wales with a population thought to number around 75,000 pairs. It mainly favours woodland habitats, but can also be found on more open farmland and even in urban parks where there are patches of trees. The Tawny is noted for the familiar "toowhit-tuwhoo" call, as well as a high pitched "kee-wick". Preying on Grey Squirrels, Magpies *Pica pica*, pigeons, small mammals and birds, and Earthworms *Lumbricas terrestres*, the Tawny Owl is highly territorial, defending an area of approximately 18–30 ha (45–75 acres) in good quality woodland. Breeding may start as early as February. As with all owls it makes no attempt to construct a nest, and usually lays its clutch of 2-4 eggs in a tree cavity, or the old stick nest of a Crow or squirrel. In areas with few trees or in woodlands where dreys and cavities are not available the eggs are sometimes laid on the ground. However, the most common site is within a tree hollow. The upright box shown here has been designed to mimic this natural site.

The eggs hatch after 30–33 days' incubation, and the young remain in the nest site for only 20–24 days. When they leave the nest they are only partially feathered, but instinctively climb into the tree canopy where they continue their development although at this stage they are still incapable of flight and are sometimes known as "branchers".

Nest Boxes

If the nest site is disturbed, Tawny Owls can be aggressive towards human intruders and to smaller birds of prey, especially Little Owls. Nesting boxes should therefore be sited with these considerations in mind.

Several designs of nesting box have proved to be suitable for Tawny Owls, but the authors have developed an upright version which is simple to install and can be attached to very young trees in areas where there are no natural cavities. Boxes should be positioned within woodland or copses, preferably a short distance in from a woodland ride or pathway which offers a natural flight path for these owls. The entrance can face south to south-east; however, local weather conditions such as prevailing winds should be the main consideration when installing these boxes.

Tawny Owls will sometimes use Kestrel boxes and Barn Owl 'A'-frame boxes. Kestrels and Barn Owls however will very rarely nest in Tawny Owl boxes because the floor space is far too small for them.

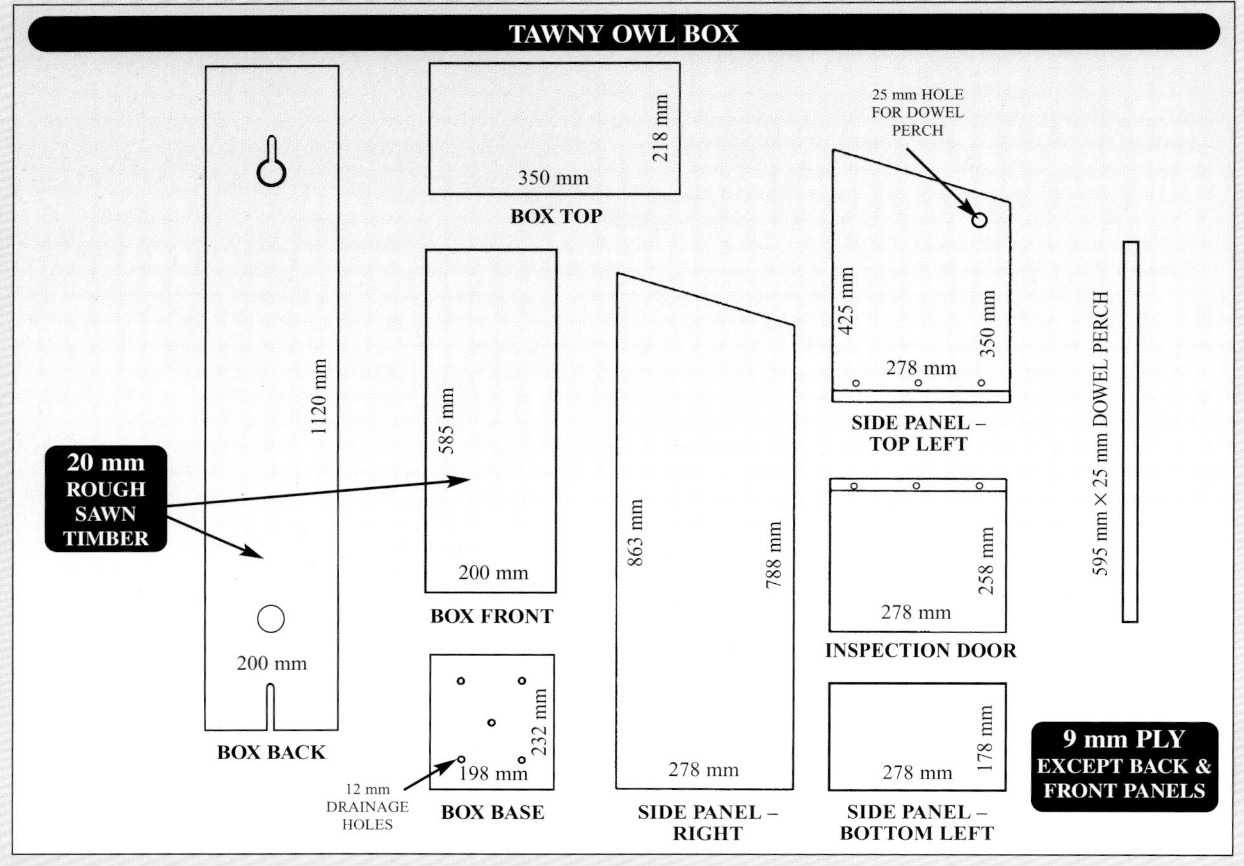

Little Owl

The Little Owl was successfully introduced into Britain from the Continent during the late 19th century. Despite periodic population decreases, especially after severe winters, the Little Owl's range has expanded to cover most of England and Wales, although it is patchily distributed in parts of the west. In Scotland it is mainly confined to the Borders, and it is absent from Ireland. The total UK population is currently thought to be between 4,000–8,500 breeding pairs. It generally occupies a farmland territory equivalent to the size of two football pitches.

Little Owls, with their piercing yellow eyes and a frowning expression, are often seen in daytime, perched on trees, fence posts or on the ground. At just 210mm (8½″) tall, this is Britain's smallest owl. Its size permits it to use much smaller hollows and tunnels than other owl species. Like other owls, it uses no nest material, but seeks readily available natural sites. These may include hollow limbs of trees, crevices in walls and farm buildings or many other types of tortuous holes, even rabbit burrows. Consequently, Little Owls can often find suitable natural sites in most areas. Nevertheless, they will use well-designed nesting boxes, though not as readily as either Tawny or Barn Owls. Little Owls, like many other birds, can suffer harassment from the larger Tawny Owl, but co-exist successfully with Barn Owls and Kestrels. They tend to favour farmland, much like Barn Owls, but unlike them are not so dependent on rough grassland. This is because they feed on invertebrates such as earthworms, moths, dor beetles, occasional small birds and mammals, many of which can be found on shorter, grazed grassland. The far-carrying "gooeek" calls of territorial males are a familiar sound in late winter and early spring, and they are uttered by day as well as night. Three to six eggs are usually laid in late April. The female incubates them for 24–25 days and the young fledge when three to four weeks old, generally in mid to late June.

Nest Boxes

Boxes can be mounted on trees *(using the mounting board shown on page 10)*. Little Owls commonly frequent farm buildings, and a box attached to an inner or outer wall can often prove successful. The box should always be provided with a good perch alongside the entrance hole. The diameter of the

entrance hole for Little Owl nesting boxes is more critical than for other owls and should be 70mm (2¾"); this allows the Little Owl access, but excludes the Tawny Owl. Little Owls like dark places so a nest chamber is incorporated in the design of the box at the back of the tunnel-like entrance.

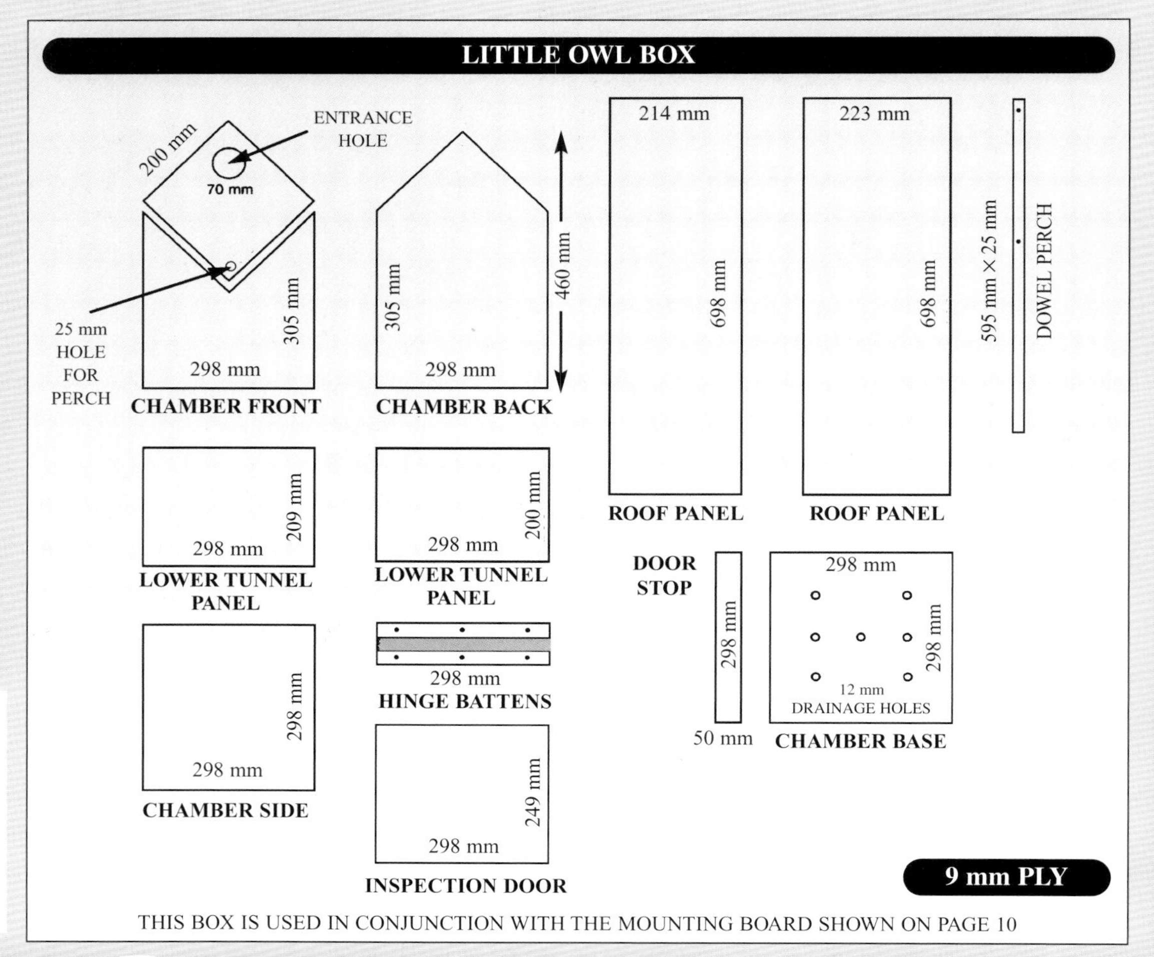

Extra strength can be provided by the incorporation of softwood battens

BASKETS

Some of our native raptors, particularly falcons and owls, choose the old stick nests of other birds or squirrel dreys in which to breed. Often the dilapidated state of many old stick nests leads to the eggs or young falling through the bottom or over the side. The smaller birds of prey such as Merlin, Hobby and Long-eared Owl are able to use the old nests of crow, Magpie and even Sparrowhawk, which are often abundant in many areas. However, in heavily keepered areas, crow nests are often destroyed to protect game.

Providing artificial nests as long-term replacements for collapsing sites, or as new sites in an area where good habitat exists but where there are no natural nesting opportunities, can help increase breeding success and hence the numbers of some birds of prey.

Materials

The use of wicker baskets as artificial nest sites for the Long-eared Owl was pioneered in Cambridgeshire by David and Don Garner with great success (see cover picture). In 1990, the authors introduced the idea of using 450mm (18″) plastic-coated wire hanging flower baskets. For a number of different birds of prey. These not only work well but provide long-term sites, since they do not decay and are cheap to purchase. The baskets can be lined with purpose-made, pre-formed cocoa-mat liners which can be purchased with the baskets. Alternatively liners can be cut out of a door mat (coir). Liners can be cable-tied into the basket and weighted down with a piece of heavy upturned turf. Alternatively the wire baskets can be woven with willow wands or fresh conifer twigs. Baskets should be positioned in a suitable tree cleft and secured with plastic cable-tie straps. The height at which the basket is positioned will vary with the species. *(See illustration, page 8.)*

Long-eared Owl

The most nocturnal of the British owls, the Long-eared Owl is commonly overlooked but for its long drawn-out hoot and the "squeaky gate" noises of the young owlets in late spring. It probably numbers about 4,000 pairs. Although it hunts over rough, open grassland for small mammals and birds, the Long-eared Owl prefers shelter belts, dense hedgerows and the edges of scrubby woodland for breeding in, using the old stick nests of Crows, Sparrowhawks *Accipiter nisus*, Magpies and Wood Pigeons *Columba palumbus*. Plastic-coated baskets for this species are best secured by using plastic cable-ties in the branches of a tree situated in a shelter-belt on open farmland, or in a tall bush. This bird has been the subject of two major research and conservation projects by The Hawk and Owl Trust.

Merlin

The Merlin is Britain's smallest falcon, numbering about 700 pairs. This moorland bird lays its eggs on the ground, usually in deep heather or rank grass, or in an isolated tree using the old stick nest of a Crow. A long-term research project by The Hawk and Owl Trust in Scotland has shown that the Merlin has adapted well to nesting in crows' nests in tall spruce trees on the edge of commercial forests. It has also shown that it can only breed successfully if large areas of moorland are retained where it can continue to hunt its main prey of small open country birds such as Meadow Pipit *Anthus pratensis* and Skylark *Alauda arvensis*.

Baskets need to be placed adjacent to open grass or heather moorland, either in a tall tree near the forest edge or in an isolated tree or bush on the moorland itself.

Hobby

The Hobby is an outstandingly fast and agile falcon resembling a Swift *Apus apus* with its pointed narrow wings. It is able to catch swifts, Swallows *Hirundo rusticolus* and martins on the wing. Insects such as moths and dragonflies are favoured during the breeding season. As a summer visitor to Britain the Hobby returns to the south of the Sahara for winter. It usually lays its eggs in an old crow's nest in a tall heathland or farmland tree. Its numbers in Britain appear to have increased and are now estimated at between 500–1000 pairs.

Unlike the Merlin, the Hobby is a bird of lowland farms and heaths. Baskets are best installed high in the crown of an isolated mature tree or in a tall tree situated in a small copse to provide a high vantage point. Sites close to water, such as a lake, river or reservoir are favoured where dragonflies and other insects are plentiful.

PLATFORMS

Unlike the owls and falcons, hawks such as the Sparrowhawk and Goshawk (as well as the Buzzard, Osprey, Red Kite, eagles and harriers) build their own nests. Even so, trees can sometimes be improved by providing a foundation platform on which the birds can be encouraged to construct their nests.

Although the provision of platforms is only relevant to a few species in Britain, the lack of safe natural tree sites capable of supporting a large and heavy nest may be limiting breeding in some raptors.

The Trust has been experimenting with the provision of nest platforms for Hen Harrier. This followed the exciting discovery of tree-nesting harriers in mature spruce plantations by The Trust's Northern Ireland representative, Don Scott. Prior to this the species has only ever been known to nest on the ground.

Materials

Waterproof platforms can be made from old discarded plastic bread trays which usually measure about 1m × 600mm (3′ × 2′) *(see page 38)*. These can be disguised with bundles of sticks cable-tied to their outside rims and the centre filled with pieces of upturned turf and stout twigs. Because they are light they are easy to lift and can be installed using long cable-ties. These platforms remain serviceable for many years. The height at which the platform is positioned will vary with the species. *(See illustration, page 8.)*

Goshawk and Buzzard

These two woodland species can sometimes benefit from the provision of a platform within the tree canopy. The Goshawk and the Buzzard both build their own nest structure. The Goshawk, which favours dense mature woodland, builds high up, close to the main trunk, and usually relies upon the radiating branches to construct its nest. The Buzzard prefers more open deciduous woodland and favours forks in trees near to open grassland, though birds in densely populated areas are even using the crowns of mature hawthorn in hedgerows.

Red Kite

Formerly very common in the UK, the species declined markedly from the 17th century onwards when it was classed as vermin and carried a bounty. In the 19th century it suffered from persecution by egg collectors and keepers so that by the beginning of the 20th century the entire British population was confined to a remote area of central Wales. Much work has been carried out and today the Red Kite is slowly re-populating Wales and, with the help of re-introduction programmes throughout England and Scotland is slowly recolonising these countries too. The Red Kite needs open country over which to hunt and scavenge, but roosts and nests in mature, usually deciduous, woodland. It builds its nest high in the fork of a tree, often using an old crow's or buzzard's nest as the base.

As yet little work has been carried out in Britain on artificial nest sites for the Red Kite, although there is every reason to suppose that the platform described for the Buzzard could attract this bird to nest.

Osprey

The Osprey became extinct in Britain in 1916. It returned to breed in Scotland in 1954 where its numbers have increased dramatically during the last 50 years with over 100 pairs now breeding annually and the population still rising. It nested in England for the first time in 2001 and has been recently introduced onto Rutland Water. It is likely that artificial platforms will be an important contribution to the future success of this bird. The

Trust has encouraged the use of such platforms on inland reservoirs in central England where Ospreys have previously stayed all summer. The Osprey platform being set in place *(on page 37)* is part of a partnership project between the Leisure Services Department of Leicester City Council and Severn Trent Water Ltd.

In other parts of the world Ospreys will nest in trees, on cliffs and even on the ground. In the Americas and central Europe, the Osprey has shown remarkable adaptability, using electricity pylons and artificial platforms mounted on telegraph poles as substitute trees. In Scotland it usually nests in the crown of prominent trees, principally Scots Pine *Pinus sylvestris* or Douglas Fir *Pseudotsuga menziesii*, close to the banks of rivers, lakes, lochs or reservoirs. Artificial sites need to be placed where there is an abundance of fish, where the landowner is sympathetic, and where the Osprey can be protected from public intrusion. Ministry of Defence land,

islands in lakes or reservoirs all provide good opportunities.

The authors have pioneered the use of two heavy-duty plastic bread trays strapped together with strong cable-ties to provide a platform about 1m × 1¼m (3′ × 4′) square. Large sticks are cable-tied in bunches around the perimeter to form a wide rim about 240mm–300mm (9″–12″) deep. This provides a 450mm (18″) diameter depression in the centre which is lined with thick divots of turf, grass and moss. Two prominent branches or dowel rods are cable-tied on one side to protrude as perches.

These perches, and the rim of the "nest", can be splashed with white emulsion paint to simulate a previously used site and make it as obvious as possible to a prospecting Osprey. The platform can be cable-tied into the crown of a Scots Pine which has been topped, and the surrounding foliage should be cut away. Alternatively it can be attached to the top of a 7m (24′) wooden pole, sandwiching the base of the bread tray between a 600mm × 450mm (2′ × 1½′) base board of exterior plywood and a pole box bracket (originally designed for the large Barn Owl pole box) using four 8mm (3″) bolts and nuts, before planting the pole at least 1½m (5′) in the ground in a suitable area close to the water's edge.

If the platform is installed by open water rich in fish on the Osprey's known migration routes through England, it is likely to offer the best opportunity for young Ospreys to stay and breed.

Useful Addresses:

For advice on grants (Set-aside, Countryside Stewardship etc.):
Countryside Agency (Tel: 01242 521381) www.countryside.gov.uk
John Dower House, Crescent Place, Cheltenham, Gloucestershire GL50 3RA
Department for Environment, Food and Rural Affairs (DEFRA) (Tel: 08459 335577) www.defra.gov.uk
3 Whitehall Place, London SW1A 2HH
Scottish Executive Rural Affairs Dept (Tel: 0131 556 8400) www.scotland.gov.uk
Pentland House, 47 Robb's Loan, Edinburgh EH14 1TW
National Assembly for Wales Agriculture Dept. (Tel: 029 20825111) www.wales.gov.uk
Cathays Park, Crown Buildings, Cardiff CF10 3NQ
Northern Ireland Executive Dept of Agriculture and Rural Development (Tel: 028 90524999) www.northernireland.gov.uk
Dundonald House, Upper Newtownards Road, Belfast BT4 3SB.
The Forestry Commission (Tel: 0131 334 0303) www.forestry.gov.uk
231 Corstorphine Road, Edinburgh EH12 7AT.
Farming and Wildlife Advisory Group (FWAG) Tel: 024 76696699 www.fwag.org.uk
National Agriculture Centre, Stoneleigh, Kenilworth, Warwickshire CV8 2RX

Countryside LicensingAgencies (for licences to inspect the nests of Schedule I birds for the purpose of monitoring or photography):
English Nature (Tel: 01733 455000) www.english-nature.org.uk
Northminster House, Peterborough PE1 1UA
Scottish Natural Heritage (Tel: 0131 447 4784) www.snh.org.uk
Countryside Council for Wales (Tel: 01248 385500) www.ccw.gov.uk
Plas Penrhos, Ffordd Penrhos, Bangor, Gwynedd LL57 2LQ
Department of the Environment, Northern Ireland Executive (Tel: 028 9025 1477) www.northernireland.gov.uk
Environment & Heritage Service, Natural Heritage, Commonwealth House, 35 Castle Street, Belfast BT1 1GU.

For advice on the law relating to birds of prey, and information on Barn Owl reintroduction:
Department for Environment, Food and Rural Affairs (DEFRA) (Tel: 0117 3728903) www.defra.gov.uk
Zone 1/08, Kite Wing, European Wildlife Division, Temple Quay House, 2 The Square, Temple Quay, Bristol BS1 6EB.

Rescue of "orphaned" birds

Occasionally young birds (particularly Tawny Owls) fall onto the ground and are picked up by well-meaning passers-by who assume that they have been abandoned. In fact the parent birds are nearly always close by and will continue to feed the youngster on the ground. Even before it is fully feathered, a young Tawny is able to climb back up the tree using its beak and talons. If such a bird is found it should be left alone, or lifted onto a nearby branch if there is thought to be immediate danger from foxes, cats, dogs or other predators.

If a young bird has been injured, or is found stranded in the middle of an open field away from an obvious nest site, it should be taken to an experienced rehabilitator who can release it back into the wild when it has recovered. The Trust, RSPCA or the local Police Wildlife Liaison Officer should be able to put you in touch with such a person.

Hand-rearing is not recommended; young birds can "imprint" upon humans very quickly, becoming totally reliant on that human as a source of food. Once this has happened it is virtually impossible to release it into the wild. It is illegal to deliberately imprint and keep a wild bird in captivity.

Disturbance of Nesting Birds

Except for the Kestrel, Sparrowhawk, Buzzard, Long-eared Owl, Little Owl and Tawny Owl, all birds of prey are listed on Schedule 1 of the Wildlife & Countryside Act 1981 or the Wildlife (Northern Ireland) Order 1985, affording them special protection. Schedule 1 species can be inspected or photographed at the nest site only by a person who has been granted a licence by the appropriate countryside agency, i.e. English Nature, Countryside Council for Wales, Scottish Natural Heritage or the Department of the Environment, Northern Ireland Executive. The Hawk and Owl Trust can provide advice about this.

Further Reading from The Hawk and Owl Trust:

- **The Barn Owl and its Habitat** (leaflet)
- **Building for Barn Owls** (leaflet)
- **Planning for Barn Owls** (leaflet)
- **The Barn Owl: The Farmer's Friend needs a Helping Hand** (booklet)
- **Forest Merlins in Scotland: Their Requirements and Management** (book)
- **Biology and Conservation of Small Falcons: Hawk and Owl Trust Conference Proceedings** (book)
- **The Long-eared Owl** (book)
- **Bird of Prey Activity Packs** (for children and schools)
- **Night of the Owls** (audio tactile pack for the blind and partially sighted)

The above titles are available from
The Hawk & Owl Trust,
c/o The Zoological Society of London,
Regent's Park, London NW1 4RY.
Please send for a price list.

ABOUT THE AUTHORS

Colin Shawyer MUniv, CBiol, FIBiol, MIEEM.

Colin is a Chartered Biologist and wildlife management and research consultant. He joined the Hawk and Owl Trust as a volunteer in 1981. The results of his Barn Owl Survey of Britain and Ireland were published six years later, when he was appointed as the Trust's Director. He provides support to the Trustees and staff and attracts, supervises and undertakes research and conservation projects for the Trust to fulfil its objects.

In 1988 he received the RSPB's annual award for *The Most Positive Contribution to Wild Birds and the Countryside*. In 1990 he gave the annual address to students of the Open University when he was honoured with Master of the University for his Barn Owl research. He also received the United Kingdom's Ford Conservation Award in 1992 after which he represented The Trust, with the Corporation of The City of London, as Britain's entry for the European Awards in Lisbon. He has since written and edited numerous books on birds of prey, has undertaken and published research papers and supervised PhD students. He strives to ensure that his conservation plan for the Barn Owl continues to grow and is monitored year by year.

Sue Dewar Dip.Rap.Biol.

Sue is a conservation consultant and raptor biologist and co-ordinated the Barn Owl Conservation Network for The Hawk and Owl Trust until February 2001 when she and her husband Richard, moved to the Isle of Mull to set up a field centre involving birds of prey. As a schoolgirl Sue read and was deeply disturbed by Rachel Carson's book *"Silent Spring"*.

An interest in falconry, conservation and rehabilitation of wild birds of prey led Sue to join The Hawk and Owl Trust in 1984, and she worked for the Trust for many years as a volunteer whilst also pursuing a Diploma course in Raptor Biology at the University of Kent. Sue was heavily involved in the organisation of The Hawk & Owl Trust's Conference on the Biology and Conservation of Small Falcons, and the joint conference run by the Trust with the Raptor Research Foundation.

Sue is now embarking on a study of Short-eared Owls on Mull.